Tom is at the book shop.

Tom likes to read books.

“Come on, Tom.”

Adam is at the toy shop.

Adam likes the toy watch.

"Come on, Adam."

Helen is at the swee

elen likes the little red sweets.

"Come on, Helen."

Mum is at the shoe shop.

Mum likes the party shoes.

"Come on, Mum."